HEY!

We've got a problem. Inside this book there's a story about a unicorn who has a surprise birthday party, complete with balloons, a cake, and even a disco ball... but this book has no pictures!

We need an illustrator to help us finish this book.

Hello! **Cris** here. I'm a Spanish illustrator, and I scribble and doodle everywhere I go. I've done a few pictures in this book to get you started, but the rest is up to you. Can you help me illustrate this entire book?

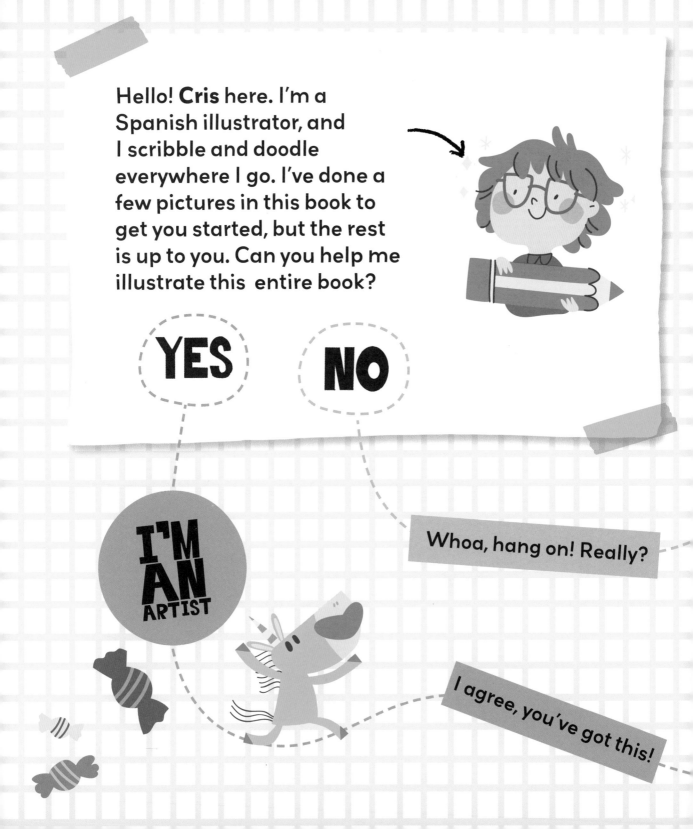

YES

NO

I'M AN ARTIST

Whoa, hang on! Really?

I agree, you've got this!

Listen, I know you can do this.
What's holding you back? Let me give you
a few tips, from one illustrator to another:

1. If you don't know where to begin, start
    drawing what you like best, or the most
    fun part. The rest will follow.

2. Get inspired. Look at art, magazines,
    posters, nature... Inspiration is everywhere.

3. There's no right or wrong with art.
    Just draw whatever makes you happy.

So, are you ready to illustrate your own book?

I'm not taking no for an answer...

Not so fast...

YES   NO

LET'S GO →

PRACTICE YOUR PEN SKILLS.

Trace...

... and color!

party time!

COLLECT IDEAS & DO RESEARCH

Try copying this drawing!

Unicorn

cake

balloon

These are some of the words that you will illustrate in this book. Look up what these words mean, and practice drawing them here!

friend

sun

Flip through the story to see who Unicorn's friends are. They all have something in common with Unicorn... a horn! Some have two horns! Try drawing them here.

shapes

BOOK PLANNER

These are all the pages in your book. Read the story first, then use this planner to sketch out your drawings for each page. It doesn't have to be perfect, just try some ideas.

Great job!
You're ready
to make your
own book.

LET'S GO ➡

THE UNICORN PARTY

Illustrated by:

_____

(you!)

Can you draw
a sunrise
outside the
window?

Unicorn slept soundly as the **sun** came up outside his **window**.

Today was a very special day.

It was Unicorn's birthday.

Downstairs, Unicorn's **friends** were planning a surprise party!

They put up **balloons** and filled the table with **food**.

Use your stickers to decorate the room!

"Wake up, Unicorn! It's party time!"

Unicorn jumped out of bed.

He put on his best outfit with **stars**, **stripes,** and **sparkly** tights.

Draw an outfit on Unicorn and don't forget the sparkles!

Unicorn's friends had each made him a present.
The gifts were all different **shapes** and **sizes!**

What did each
friend make?
Can you draw
the presents?

Out came a **big rainbow cake!**

"I can see red, orange, yellow, green, blue, indigo, and violet! What a beautiful cake!" said Unicorn.

He blew out the **candles.**

Whooooooosh!

How old is Unicorn today? Add candles and color the cake!

Finish
drawing
these
animals!

The friends played a party game. They each drew their favorite **animal** and everyone had to guess what it was.

Unicorn drew a **wombat!**

Did you know that wombat poop is square? Draw a little poop!

Time to **dance!**

The **disco ball** spun
around and lit up the room.

Look at Unicorn's dance moves!
Everyone tried to copy them.

Whoa! Can you draw
Unicorn dancing?
Who is copying him?

What is
Unicorn
dreaming?

That night, Unicorn went to sleep thinking about his kind friends...

... and wondering what dance moves to try at his next birthday!

One year later...

This page is all yours!
Draw the sequel to
this story. What
happens at Unicorn's
next birthday?

THE
END

(Not!)

Congratulations! You've done an **amazing job** of illustrating this book. But it's not over yet. Now that you have made your very own book, you can **display it** somewhere, give it to someone as a present, or **make more books** and set up a bookshop in your bedroom! Whatever you do, be sure to **share your work** with the world because your creativity will **inspire others.** It's been great working with you!

Learning Guide

Hi, grown-ups!

The *ILLUSTRATE THIS BOOK* series empowers children to explore literacy through drawing.

We know that drawing is a powerful learning tool. It can help children build confidence and strengthen visual literacies while supporting them to reach their reading and writing milestones.

As your child completes this book they will use their own ingenuity to develop three crucial elements of literacy:

- Vocabulary
- Reading comprehension
- Visual literacy

You may find that your child needs support for the practice and research pages at the start of the book. That's a great way for you to collaborate and help them plan.

On the story pages, encourage them to take the lead and come up with ideas for illustrating the pages. This is where their imaginations can shine.

Don't be afraid to draw, too. We often hear adults say, "I can't draw!" But there is no right or wrong with art. If you sketch a chicken and it looks like a frog, you've invented a new animal. That's your creativity at work.